The crow's nest is the highest part of the main mast of a ship, that is used as a lookout point to spot the enemy approaching! In the early 19th century, it was just a barrel or a basket lashed to the tallest mast, but later became a specially designed platform.

A **poop deck** is the roof of a cabin built in the rear part of the ship, making it an ideal place to navigate and watch the crew were behaving themselves!

Rigging is the term used to describe the system of ropes, chains and tackle used to support and control the masts and sails of a ship.

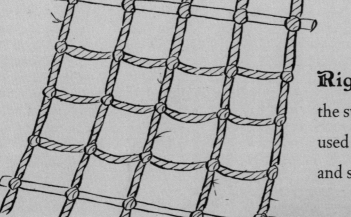

For all the wonderful staff and volunteers at the Wiltshire Scrapstore who gather scrap like the best of pirates and turn it into glistening treasure.

Neil x

Red Robin BOOKS
Where story matters

Red Robin Books is an imprint of Corner To Learn Limited

Published by
Corner To Learn Limited
Willow Cottage • 26 Purton Stoke
Swindon • Wiltshire SN5 4JF • UK

ISBN: 978-1-908702-12-8

First published in the UK 2014
Text © Neil Griffiths 2014
Illustrations © Janette Louden 2014

The rights of Neil Griffiths and Janette Louden to be identified as the authors of this work has been asserted by them in accordance with the Copyright, Designs and Patents Act 1988.

Design by David Rose

Printed in China

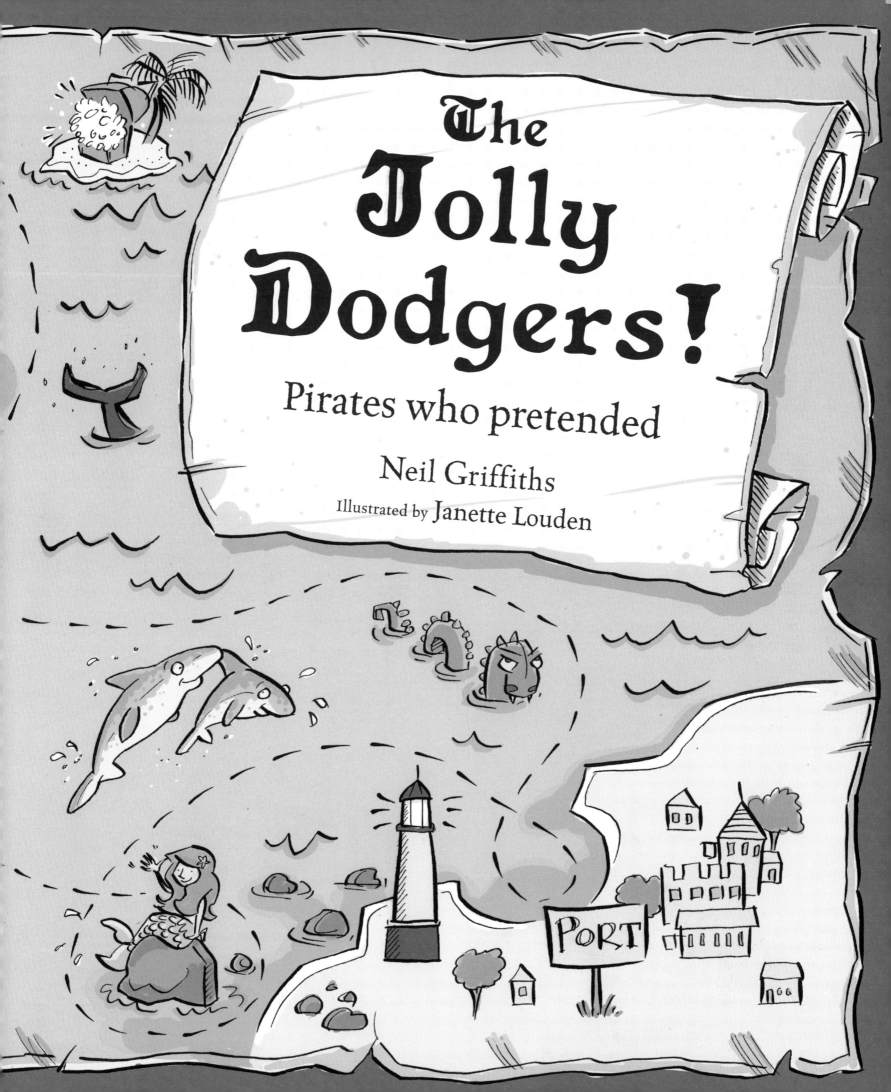

The Jolly Dodgers!

Pirates who pretended

Neil Griffiths

Illustrated by Janette Louden

PORT

This is a tale from long ago, when savage **pirates** ruled the seas. It was a time when innocent sailing **galleys** laden with **treasures** were set upon by **swashbuckling vagabonds**.

These **blaggards** brought their pirate ships **broadside** and blasted masts with their whizzing **cannonballs**, boarded with **grappling hooks** and slashed the **main sails** with their razor-sharp **cutlasses** (usually shouting, **"Ahoy there, me mateys,"** in vicious tones).

Once on board, they dangled some of the **crew** by their toes from the **crow's nest** to scare them, **keelhauled** others to terrify them, then forced them all to **walk the plank** and be left to the mercy of circling sharks! (Not that many were very merciful!)

The ship was then **plundered** of its glittering treasures as the pirates sang "**Yo, ho, ho and a bottle of rum!**" before being sunk without trace.

Then as quickly as a ship's rat could run up the **rigging**, the pirates would disappear with their loot into the murky night.

Such ships were captained by cruel ruthless leaders such as **Blood-curdler Bill** and **Gordon the Gizzard-gouger**, to mention but two. Even the very names of their ships, **The Jolly Bone Snapper** and **The Galley Gut Churner**, sent shivers down the timbers of many a seafarer's spine!

GORDON THE GIZZARD-GOUGER

BLOOD-CURDLER BILL

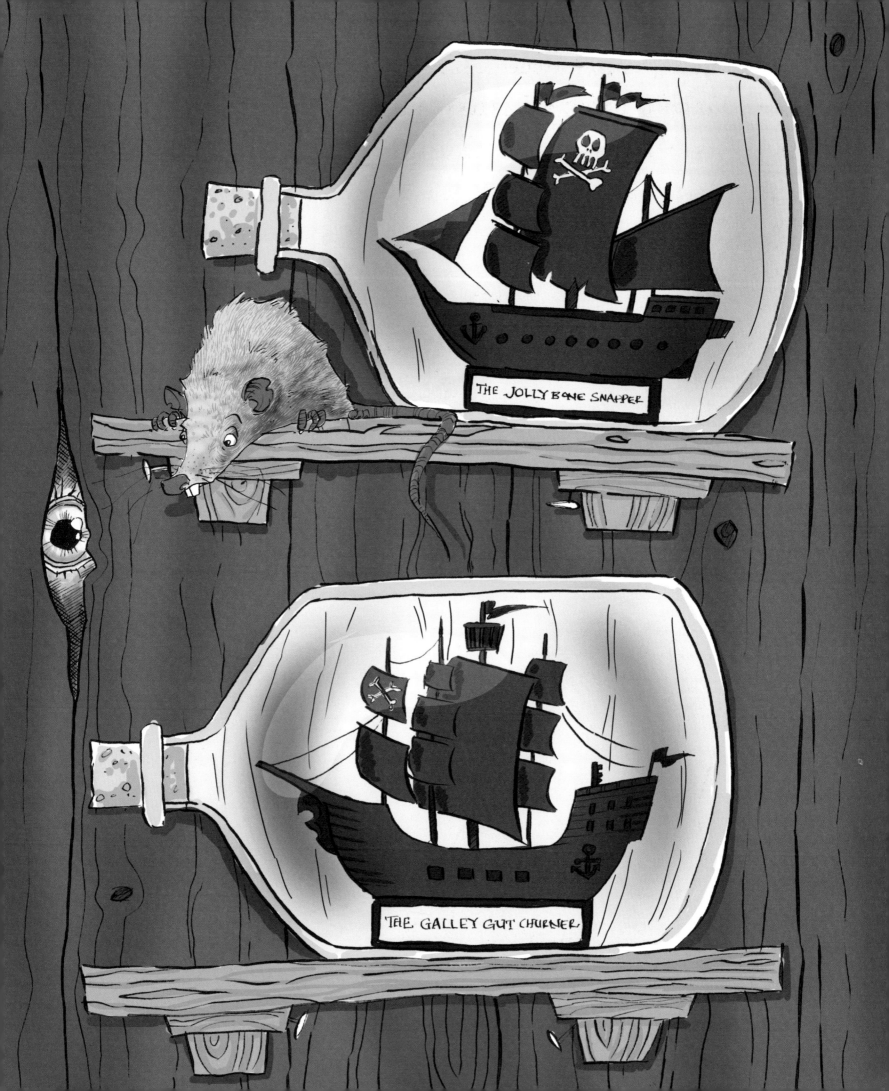

But one pirate **crew** led a very different life to most. They were forced to become pirates and were sent out to sea in search of **swag** by their bossy wives (who certainly ruled the crow's nests). The wives craved for jewellery that glistened and shone like a **buccaneer's button** (and by the look of them, they certainly needed the help of something dazzling).

But this band of puny sea swaggers did all they could to avoid any encounters of a rough kind. Despite their names, the captain **Knuckleduster Red**, the ship's cook **Cannibal Cliff**, the ship's doctor **Chop-it-off Charlie**, the ship's navigator **Big-eyed Bill** and the ship's deckhands **Knee-knobbler Nick**, **Toe-trapper Tim** and **Skull-cracker Cuthbert**, the last thing they wanted to do was fight.

KNUCKLEDUSTER NED (THE CAPTAIN)

Named after his dusting skills, not his knuckles!

BIG-EYED BILL

Who could spot an enemy ship five miles away.

KNEE-KNOBBLER NICK

Who has been voted 'The Most Knobbly-kneed Pirate of the Year' for six years in a row.

In fact, the minute a ship was spotted on the horizon, they would

scarper into the nearest patch of fog which was as thick as pirates' porridge!

Whilst their wives believed their brave marauding husbands were fighting ferociously out at sea, in reality they were doing the opposite!

Well, blow me down with a sailor's **hornpipe**, this is them **anchored** up in the bay of an exotic tropical island. Not exactly a hard life, is it? The only terrifying thing about this lot of **hornswogglers** is their underwear hanging from the **rigging!**

Why, it's more like a luxury cruise liner than a rotten old rat-ridden pirate ship! This is hardly walking the plank, is it? The **blaggards!**

Not the knot-tying expected of a pirate, is it?

Mopping the deck? More like mop mincing!

Ship's wheel or wheel of fortune?

Why, these are for boat-blasting, not bowling. (Outrageous!)

These **grapplers** are for crawling on board ships loaded with loot, not for catching crabs!

This crow's nest should be renamed peacock's paradise! (A disgrace to piratehood!)

Those sails should be set for stormy seas,

not used as slopes for sea surfing!

Talk about
pirate pampering!

(Preposterous!)

"Come in, number six, your time is up!"
(This must be an illegal use of pirate property?!)

Why look, even the ship's cat has
cosied up with the ship's rats!
(Unbelievable!)

But all good things must surely come to an end. How could such a life of luxury last any longer?

Well, as each time this pathetic bunch of **sea dogs** returned to **port**, their furious wives sent them back out to sea again in search of luxurious treasures. And of course that's just what that bunch of **weevils** wanted!

This happened again and again, until two of the wives thought it was high time they had someone tougher and rougher on board, capable of some real pirate-pounding.

So they sneaked up the **gangplank** and, with a bit of a struggle, stowed away on board in some large empty **rum barrels**.

But if it was blood-curdling action they were looking for, what they found was just blood-boiling. What they saw was more than any pirate's wife could stand. In fact, their enraged faces caused the rats, cats, weevils, fleas and captain's parrot to **scuttle** from the ship.

They started gently with a little unpleasant name-calling such as "**Lily-livered landlubbers**", "**Big bunch of bilge rats**" and "**Pathetic pile of poop-deckers**", not to mention "**Scurvy-scabbed swabs**".

But then things got really nasty as the pirate-pulverising really started. This was only the beginning of their punishment, as once back in port, they received a repeat performance!

Eventually, this battered bunch of pretend pirates were banished from the high seas permanently and assigned to domestic duties of the worst type.

In fact, they spent the rest of their lives **swabbing** decks, bailing out **bilges** and setting sails of a very different kind.

As for their wives. Well, they replaced their husbands and took themselves out to sea …
… and the last thing you could say is that they were **pretending** to be pirates! But that's a **sea-swagging** story for another day!

Keelhauling was a nasty form of punishment dished out to badly behaved sailors. They were tied to a rope and dragged from one side of the ship to the other, through the water under the keel. It hurt!

A **gangplank** is a board or a ramp that is used as a removable footway between a ship and the dock.

An anchor is used to secure a ship in the water and stop it drifting in the current or wind. Made from metal, it is attached to a chain or strong rope which is connected to the ship. Once released into the water, it is allowed to hook into the sea bed.